With lo[ve]

Lau[...]

From

Kinda

Sept. 91   xx 🙂

OUR PLANET

OUR PLANET

BY

M. B. GOFFSTEIN

CANONGATE

First published in Great Britain in 1988
by Canongate Publishing Limited, Edinburgh

Published in the United States in 1979 by
Farrar Straus & Giroux, New York

British Library Cataloguing in Publication Data
Goffstein, M. B.
Our Planet.
I. Title
813'.54[J]

ISBN 0 86241 209 9

Printed and bound by
MacLehose and Partners, Portsmouth

TO BARLA

Our planet is a lively ball
in the universe.

Oceans move ceaselessly,
and below, in the deep,

fish swim, molluscs hop,
and plants wave silently.

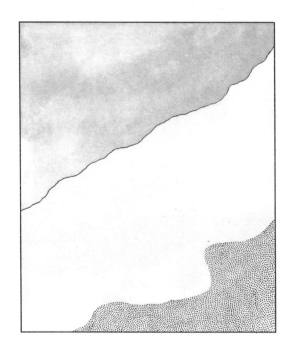

Tiny grains of sand
keep the powerful waters
from flooding lands

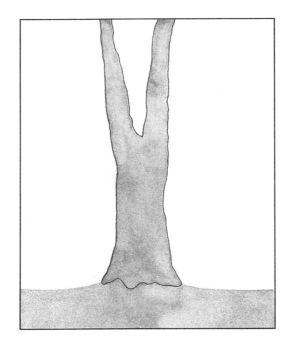

where trees grow skyward.

It looks so peaceful
from afar.

But little puffs of smoke
erupt
where men are fighting,

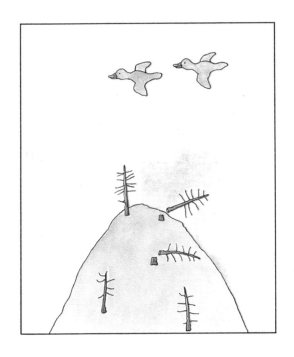

or shooting ducks
down from the sky,
or breaking mountains.

Homeless dogs and cats
are scared and lonely.

Old people look in dustbins
hopefully,

though we have riches
we are born to share.

Low trees hold fruit

and vegetables lie warmly
in the soil
or hide on vines.

Waves of wheat and corn
shimmer in the sun.
They are made for people.

They're made for cows
who nurse their calves.

They're made for grey wolves
with their pups.

They're made for ducks
and singing birds and snakes
and little minks.

Every living creature
is our brother and our sister,

dearer than the jewels
at the centre of the earth.

So let us be
like tiny grains of sand,

and protect all life
from fear and suffering!

Then, when the stars shine,
we can sleep in peace,

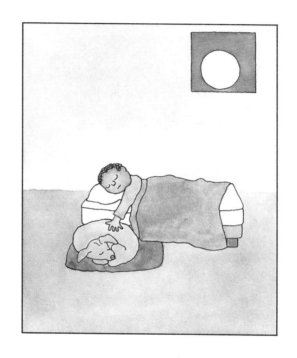

with the moon
as our quiet night-light.